★・S·I·X·T·Y・★

SILLY JOKES YOU CAN PLAY ON YOUR FRIENDS

(Hardcover title: The Surprise Book)

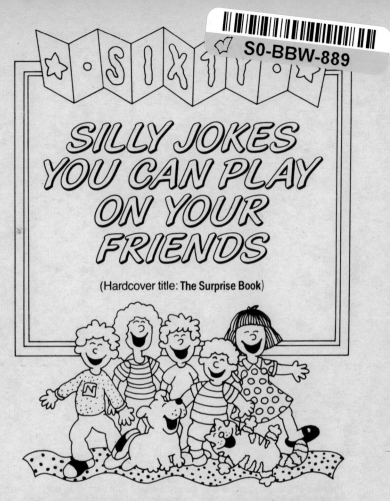

by LAURENCE B. WHITE, JR. & RAY BROEKEL

Inside Illustrations by
Will Winslow

SCHOLASTIC INC.
New York Toronto London Auckland Sydney Tokyo

Some editorial changes have been made by the authors for this
Scholastic edition.

ISBN 0-590-32402-0

12 11 10 9 8 7 6 5 4 3 2   7 8/8
                  Printed in the U.S.A.   28

Contents

1
YOU BETTER WATCH IT!

Do this please:
    Hold your nose.
    Tight.
    Say "Iced ink" out loud.
    Say it again.
    "Iced ink."
    Keep holding your nose . . .
    . . . keep saying "Iced ink."
    You'll catch on soon!

The tricks in this chapter are quick tricks that might just surprise YOU.

We'll Bet You . . .

We'll Bet You Can't . . .
>   We'll bet you can't
>   can't read all the
>   the words in this
>   this paragraph right
>   right the very first
>   first time!

We'll Bet You Can't . . .
>   Give us a definition for
>   a SPIRAL STAIRCASE
>   an ACCORDION
>   the HULA DANCE
without moving your arms, hands, or body the
slightest bit.

. . . We'll bet your friends can't either!

Make This Bow and Arrow Go

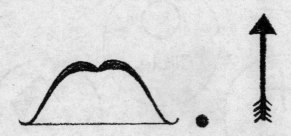

Would you like to shoot the bow and arrow? You can—right out of this book!

Touch your nose to the dot between the bow and arrow and focus your eyes on the pictures. You can focus your eyes so the arrow looks as though it is *in* the bow, ready for firing.

Ready, now. With your eyes still focused and your nose still touching the dot, *twist the book around toward the left* (counterclockwise).

. . . TWANG!

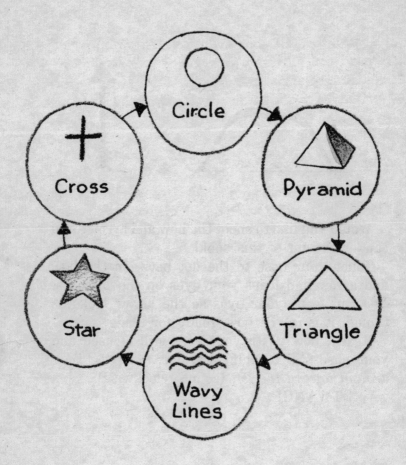

Strange Symbols

We have ESP and we'll prove it, if you'll help. Please concentrate on any one of the six symbols inside the large circles.

Got one? Good. Now don't tell which symbol you picked, just follow these directions carefully.

Place your finger on the circle symbol. Now move your finger to the pyramid and spell the first letter of your symbol to yourself. Move your finger to the triangle and spell the second letter. Move from symbol to symbol as you spell the letters in the name of your symbol.

When you're done spelling, we'll know what symbol you were thinking of because you will end right on it!

Don't you agree that we have ESP—Extra Surprise Power? Try it again, use another symbol. We never fail.

The Old Swap Trick

Try this right now and we'll bet you can't figure out how it works.

Lay three pennies and a paper clip right over these pictures.

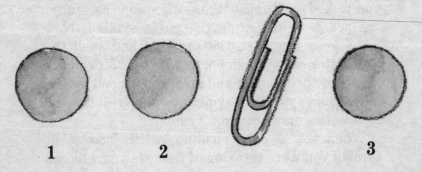

1   2   3

Now we will ask you to swap the paper clip with one of the coins. You will have a free choice as to which side you swap on, but you must follow one rule: *You must always swap the paper clip with one of the coins that is right beside it.*

Now: 1. Swap the clip and a coin.
              2. Swap the clip again.
              3. Swap it again.
              4. Swap it again.
              5. Swap it again.

You have now had a chance to swap the paper clip with a coin five times.

Now take away coin number 1.

Swap the clip one last time.

Now you have had six chances to make a swap.

HOW COME THE PAPER CLIP IS BACK IN THE SAME PLACE IT STARTED FROM? *WE* made you do it! Can you figure out how?

Math-A-Magic

OUR number is 8. Will you remember that?
Now, you think of any number between 1 and 10.
That will be YOUR number.
Now do some math for us.

Double YOUR number.
Add 2.
Multiply the answer by 5.
Subtract 2.
Write the total on a piece of paper.

Hey, wait a minute. I see OUR number in your total . . . and isn't the rest of the total YOUR number?
How could that be?

A Great Surprise

QUICK! Look at the bottom of this page and you will find a stupendously silly surprise!

A stupendously silly surprise!

Are You Right or Left Thumbed?

That's right, *thumbed!* Which are you? Want to find out?

Bring your two hands together and interlace your fingers. Your thumbs will lay one on top of the other. Whichever one lays on *top* is what "thumbed" you are. If your right thumb is on top, you are "right-thumbed." If your left one is on top you are "left-thumbed."

You don't believe it? Try placing your thumbs the other way. It *feels* wrong and very strange, doesn't it?

Run a check on your family and friends. Are most of them right- or left-thumbed? Can you find a left-handed person who is right-thumbed? There are such people.

One-Eyed Surprise

Each of your eyes sees a separate picture. Your brain blends the two pictures together and creates a single picture of what you see.

Press your nose against a mirror and focus your eyes on your eyes reflected in the glass. It will be hard to focus, but, even blurry, what do you think you will see?

Your right eye sees only the mirror image of itself. Your left eye sees only your left eye. Each eye sees an eye, *but only one eye.* Your brain will blend the pictures from each eye together. Do you think it will create a picture of you, but with only one eye right in the middle of your forehead? That's worth trying . . . just to find out!

Be Two Years Old Again

Place your finger on "A" and trace the line down to "B." Easy. But easy because your eyes, brain, and muscles have been working together for a good number of years. This kind of teamwork is called your *coordination*.

When you were two years old you were not as coordinated. Here's how to remember what it was like:

Hold the drawing next to a mirror. Look into the mirror. Place your finger on "A" and trace to "B" just as you did before, except this time *do it while looking in the mirror*. The reversed picture in the mirror confuses your brain and makes it difficult to coordinate the muscles in your arm and hand.

Of course, with practice, you can learn to do it—just the way a two-year-old learns to draw and move gracefully. Time, practice, and teamwork!

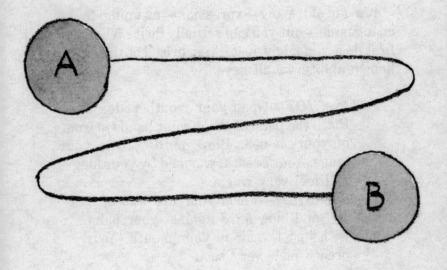

Do You Blow Hot and Cold?

It's an old slang expression—meaning to be changeable—but you can actually do it. When you first do it you might just be surprised at this little-known ability we all have.

To blow HOT—Open your mouth wide.
    Place the palm of one of your hands in front of your mouth. Blow *gently*, from your lungs. Your breath, warmed by your lungs, will feel very warm.

To blow COLD—Form your lips into a tight "O" and blow *hard* against your palm with just the air in your mouth. Your breath feels very cool.

With a simple change of the shape of your mouth you become the strange creature who blows "hot and cold" whenever you choose!

Here's Your Age

Here are five columns showing people's ages from 1 to 31. Which columns show your age?

1	2	4	8	16
3	3	5	9	17
5	6	6	10	18
7	7	7	11	19
9	10	12	12	20
11	11	13	13	21
13	14	14	14	22
15	15	15	15	23
17	18	20	24	24
19	19	21	25	25
21	22	22	26	26
23	23	23	27	27
25	26	28	28	28
27	27	29	29	29
29	30	30	30	30
31	31	31	31	31

Now we are going to tell you how old you are. You must help us just a bit.

Add together the first numbers of each of the columns that shows your age. Just the first numbers in each. Have you added them together? Good. That's your age, isn't it?

Can You Write Your Own Name?

Want to try something that's easy? Sit at a table and write your name on a sheet of paper.

Now try something that's almost impossible. Sit at a table and write your name on a piece of paper while you're doing the following:

Cross your legs under the table and begin moving the foot of the leg that's on top in a little circle. Keep the foot rotating in a circle as you try to write your name.

2
STRANGE THINGS HAPPEN

Wet a facecloth with warm water.
Hold the facecloth by one corner, and
spin it around fast ten times.
Touch the warm (?) facecloth to your face.
SURPRISE. . .

You won't believe what the warm facecloth feels
like.

It is definitely *not* warm!

All of the experiments and tricks in this chapter
will require a little "getting ready"—but you will
find every one will surprise YOU!

A Bright Face

On a separate piece of paper draw a picture of the face of a clock. Show the numbers but do not draw in any hands.

Now play "connect the numbers." First try to "see" the picture with your mind, then use a pencil to see if you were right.

Draw a line:
> From 10:00 to   2:00
> From   8:00 to 12:00
> From   4:00 to 10:00
> From   2:00 to   8:00
> From 12:00 to   4:00

You should have drawn a star!

The Soup-Can Race

The next time you have a can of soup for lunch you can discover the solution to this surprising experiment.

Wash out the can with water and dry it. You will also need another can, the same size, that is still full of soup.

Place the two cans end to end (but not quite touching) on the floor. Give them a push—together—and let them roll across the floor.

One can is full of soup. One can is empty. They start side by side, how do they finish?

ONE will always win this race!

Which one? The full or the empty goes farther and faster. Which one?

Sorry! No answer here! You'll just have to save a soup can and find out!

Name That Face

Did you ever face your name? That is, did you ever make a face with your name? Perhaps the easiest way to understand what we mean is by trying it.

First, draw a cartoon head without a face.

Turn the paper sideways and write your signature (first or last name only) across the "face."

Now turn the paper so it is right way up. Some names make great faces, some look awfully stupid. How about yours?

The Trick Question Quiz

The following test is not one you will recieve in school! Every question is a "trick" question and only the trickiest of tricky people ever score 100. Now, watch out . . .

1. Do they have a 4th of July in England?

2. Take 2 apples from 3 apples and what do you have?

3. How many birthdays does the average person have?

4. A farmer had 11 chickens. All but 9 died. How many chickens were left?

5. How many animals of each kind did Moses take aboard the ark?

6. If a plane from France crashed on the border of the United States, where would the survivors be buried?

7. What planet is closest to us at the present time?

8. Some months have 31 days, some 30 days. How many have 28 days?

9. I have two coins which equal 55¢. One is not a nickel, what are the two coins?

10. Does half of 2 plus 2 equal 2 . . . or 3?

Answers

1. Of course! They may not celebrate it, but they have a July 4 on their calendar.
2. YOU have 2 apples because that's what you took.
3. We all have the same number of birthdays—only one.
4. All but 9 died so these 9 must still be left.
5. *Moses* took no animals on any ark—were you thinking of Noah?
6. Survivors are never buried because they are still alive.
7. The planet Earth is right under your feet.
8. Every month has (at least) 28 days.
9. A half dollar and a nickel. We said *one* is not a nickel and the half dollar is the one.
10. This is a question everyone gets right because you can use either answer:
    Half of 2 is 1, plus 2 equals *3*.
    Half of 2 + 2 (4) equals *2*.

Mirror Magic

LOOK AT THIS PAGE UPSIDE DOWN IN A MIRROR

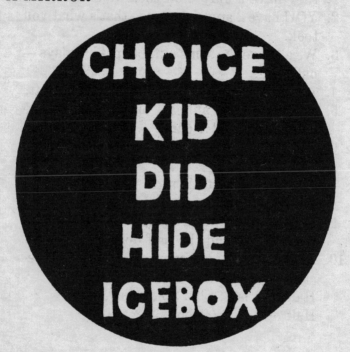

CHOICE
KID
DID
HIDE
ICEBOX

SURPRISE! The words in the
circle still are the right
way around. Only

Fog in the Summertime . . . or Anytime

Have you ever seen your breath on a cold winter day? Tiny droplets of water in your warm breath gather together and you see them as *fog*. You can make the droplets gather anytime of year if you know how. . .

Try this right now:
1. Go outdoors in the bright sun or stand in a well-lighted area.
2. Fill your mouth with air. Let your cheeks bulge out.
3. Cover your mouth with your open hand and press hard.
4. BLOW HARD against your hand but don't let any air get out of your mouth.
5. Stop blowing. Remove your hand. Open your mouth and let your breath out slowly. As your breath comes out, look at it. FOG!

. . . And now you can do it anytime, anyplace, for yourself, your friends, or an audience of thousands!

——3——
WEIRD AND WONDERFUL WORDS

A-E-I-O-U—the vowels!
Can you think of a word that contains all of them?
UNQUESTIONABLY!

And . . .
Can you spell a word that everybody spells wrong?
WRONG! Right?

Surprising Signs

RESTAURANT

Eat Now. . . .
Pay Waiter

SUPERMARKET

7 Days Without
Food
Makes One Weak

GROUCHVILLE

Everyone is
Welcome Here
. . . Except YOU!

NUDIST CAMP

Open
We Never Clothe

SCHOOL ZONE

Use Your Eyes
Save the Pupils

MUSIC STORE

Closed
Gone Chopin

You Are?

How are you at spelling? Prove it. Spell the following words out loud for us. After you spell each one say, "Light bulb."

Spell *bright*. Then say "Light bulb."
Spell *red*. Then say "Light bulb."
Now spell *pretty*. Don't forget to say "Light bulb."

And finally—here's the tough one—spell the word *image*. Remember, "Light bulb."

You are? That's funny, you sure don't look like one!

Silly Stuff About You

Do you know that if your nose were twelve inches long it would be a foot?

If your nose runs and your feet smell then you must be upside down!

Your pants are always too short because you have two feet sticking out the bottom!

"Yes" is an answer you can never give if you are asked "Are you asleep?"

Your underwear is your only clothing that is never worn out!

People have four feet . . . when there are two of them!

The hardest thing you will find about learning to ride a bicycle is the sidewalk!

"Quiet" is the only thing you break when you say it!

You can easily drop an egg six feet without breaking it, if you drop it off a seven-foot ladder!

Six things that contain milk are cheese, butter, ice cream, you (after eating any one of them), and two cows!

Money Madness

Would you like to go crazy? Take the test that follows. If you make it all the way through you have an extremely good mind. If you don't, then you're like the rest of us!

1. On a separate sheet of paper write *dollar*.

2. If a dime is more than a nickel write *nickel* to the left of *dollar*.

3. If there are more pennies in a dime than quarters in a dollar don't write *penny* under *nickel* unless a nickel is more than a penny.

4. Now cross out *dollar* and write *quarter* under it only if there are more dimes in a half dollar than nickels in a quarter; otherwise write *quarter* over *dollar*.

5. If there are more quarters in a nickel than nickels in a quarter don't cross out *nickel* but cross out *quarter* instead.

6. Draw a line under *dollar* and write *dime* to the right of it only if a dime has as many pennies as a dollar has dimes.

7. If you have not crossed out *nickel* cross out *dime* unless you have crossed out *dime*, in which case write the number of quarters in a dollar under *dollar*.

8. Finally, be sure to cross out *dime* if you have not underlined *dollar* and cross out dollar unless you have not underlined *dime*.

Now we will be give you the answer to this test. If your answer does not look like this then we *dare* you to go back and find out where you went wrong.

~~nickel~~
penny

quarter
dollar

~~dime~~

Aren't you glad your teachers don't give this kind of test?

Think About These

"My mother wanted me to be a fortune-teller, but I couldn't see any future in it."

Do you know that it's bad luck to be superstitious?

I never make mistooks!

"Do you believe in astrology?"
"Of course not. I'm a Virgo and only Scorpios believe in astrology!"

Do you know that only stupid people say only stupid people say only stupid people say only stupid people say . . .

Want to drive a friend crazy? Write a letter on one sheet of paper—but write Page 2 at the top!

Letter Tell a Story

To read these stories you must say the letters out loud. C D B sounds like "See the bee." See if you can understand the entire story.

C D B?

S I C D B.

N D B Cs U.

O!

G!

I I I I I I I!!!

And another:

Do U C D Pup-E?

S I C D Pup-E.

D Pup-E likes U.

O N I like D Pup-E.

I M ver-E hap-E.

So S D Pup-E!

Can You?

WHICH THRUSH WHISTLES

Surprise! You cannot say these words out loud three times very fast without making a mistake.

Try it.

Weird and Wonderful Words

If $\dfrac{\text{I'M MAD}}{\text{YOU}}$ means "I'm mad over you"...

and GEG is a "scrambled egg"...

What do these weird words mean?

1) ORC HE'S TRAW

2) talk

3) ƎʞⱯↃ

4) THE ST^RE_E_T

5) YOU-ᒐᘴƧT-ME

6) STORY

7) ⅁NIʞOO⅃

8) 1 2 3 4 5 6 ⁷ 8 9

9) FRIENDS $\left(\dfrac{\text{STANDING}}{\text{A MISS}}\right)$ FRIENDS

10) LEM
ADE

1. He's in the Orchestra
2. Small talk
3. Upside-Down Cake
4. A bump in the street
5. Just between you and me
6. A tall story
7. Looking backward
8. 7-Up
9. A misunderstanding between friends
10. Lemonade

35

A Nose Without a Face

We are going to ask you to say something right now out loud. We bet you can't do it.

Say, out loud, A nose without a face.
Did you say "A nose without a face"?
You said it wrong.
Try again.
Say a nose without a face.
Did you say "A nose without a face"?
You did it again. You're still wrong.
Try once again: A nose without a face.
"A nose without a face"—still wrong!

You are not paying close attention. We asked you to say "a nose"—without a face. In other words you should only say "a nose"—*nothing else*. That way you are saying it without (saying) "a face." Get it? . . . Got it? . . . GOOD!

You-Had-Better-Watch-It Words

A POST is a pole in the ground.
A ROAST is meat in the oven.
MOST is what you have a lot of.
BOAST is what you brag about.
Now, quickly, spell what you put in a toaster and eat for breakfast.

Sorry . . . TOAST is what you take *out* of a toaster. We asked what you put *in*. That's b-r-e-a-d!

Got the idea? To spell these answers you have to watch it or you might just make a mistake. Try another.

Spell TEN.
Spell TEN again.
Once more spell TEN.
Now, quickly, spell what aluminum cans are made of.

Sorry, not TIN. Aluminum cans are made from a-l-u-m-i-n-u-m!

4

YOU DO IT

Touch the tips of your forefingers together. Press them *hard* against each other.

Ask a friend to grasp your wrists. Tell your friend to try and pull your fingers apart.

As your friend tries, you press hard.

The amazing thing is that your friend cannot separate your fingers!

You probably won't believe it until you do it, so do it!

How to Tattoo You

Want a lion on your legs? Palms on your arms? Lace all over your face? Or "jelly" written on your belly?

Then you really must learn the art of instant tattooing. That way you can put words and pictures anywhere you wish at any time. And they will wash off easily later.

Take a small scrap of paper and draw a picture on it with a *soft* lead pencil. Trace over the lines several times so they are nice and thick.

Now wet the spot on your skin where you want to place the tattoo. Use a damp cloth or tissue and be sure your skin is very wet.

Place the pencil picture, line side down, against your wet skin. SLAP the palm of your hand down on the picture. This will stick it tight so it can't move or smudge.

RUB the paper a few times hard with your fingertips.

PEEL the paper off carefully.

Your tattoo is done and is now on you!

If you use words, they must be written backward. Here's an easy way to do it. First write the words forward on thin paper. Turn the paper over and copy the words through the paper. They will copy backward. Use the backside for your tattoo. The backward words will come out right way around on your skin.

Make One of Your Arms Shorter Than the Other

When we were first shown this trick we didn't believe it could happen. When we first tried it, it didn't work. Then we tried it again—and we just couldn't believe our eyes!

Stand facing a wall. Stretch your arms out in front of you until your fingertips just touch the wall. Move closer or farther from the wall so your arms are really stretched out straight.

The fingertips of *both* hands will just touch the wall because both of your arms are the same length, right? Well, not for long . . .

Bend your right arm up and rub the elbow *very hard* with your left hand. Rub really hard and count slowly to 25.

When you are done reach out with your arms again and touch the wall with your fingertips . . .

But wait. *Your left hand touches first!*

Your right arm seems to have shortened. If it doesn't happen the first time, try it again. Why does it happen? We don't have the faintest idea!

By the way, your arms will somehow return to the correct length the very next time you wish to try this experiment—or maybe it was just some kind of optical illusion in the first place.

Side by Side

This trick requires a shuffled deck of playing cards. Get a deck now and shuffle it well, but don't look at the faces of the cards as you do.

We are now going to make a magic prediction. *Somewhere in that deck you have put either a queen beside a three or an ace beside a five!*

Don't believe us? Take a look. Remember that hearts, spades, diamonds, and clubs don't matter. Just look for a queen beside a three and an ace beside a five.

Amazingly, you will probably find this has happened. If not, give us one more chance. Shuffle the deck again and look one more time.

If you still don't find one of the pairs, look for a nine and a two. We "feel" a nine and two might also be together!

The Betcha-Can't-Catch-It Trick

Will you take this bet? We will drop a sheet of ordinary paper from six feet and you must catch it between your finger and thumb before it touches the floor. We betcha can't. Will you betcha can?

Watch it! WE have the best chance of winning.

DO THIS: Hold a sheet of paper (not cardboard) in one of your hands. Hold the paper as high up as you can and let it go.

The paper will flutter back and forth as it slowly falls to the floor. Looks as if it would be a snap to catch.

Try to catch it with your other hand using only your forefinger and thumb.

If you do catch it you are very quick.

Betcha can't do it three times in a row.

Betcha your friends can't do it either!

The Automatic Big Bubble Blower

Your mother will love this trick. That's because it works best when you're washing the dishes! (Of course, you could cheat and do it when nobody's in the kitchen.)

You're washing the dishes and you notice that the plastic squeeze soap bottle is about half empty.

Squeeze a bit of soap into the water but don't stir it in. Touch your finger to the floating blob of soap and then touch your soapy fingertip to the top of the soap bottle.

The bottle is your automatic bubble blower. Squeeze it gently. A bubble will appear. Keep squeezing. See how large you can make the bubble.

You'll find that the easier you squeeze, the larger the bubble. A quicker squeeze makes lots of tiny bubbles. They're fun too.

When you've made a big bubble, try to blow it off. If you blow easy you will have a great big gorgeous bubble floating gracefully over the sink.

It's a neat trick. Even your mom won't complain as long as you're washing the dishes at the same time. And this trick really does make washing the dishes just a little bit of fun!

The Band on Your Hand

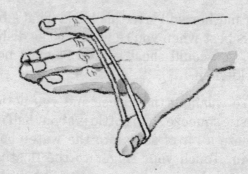

Find a small rubber band.

Turn either of your hands over so you are looking at the back. Loop the band over your hand so it goes across the back from the little finger to your thumb. Pull it down so it is *below all* of your knuckles.

Now you're ready. Here are the rules:

You cannot use your other hand.

You cannot rub the band on anything.

You can only move your fingers and wrist.

What do you do? You try to take the band off. But we bet you can't, no matter how much you wiggle, twist, squiggle, or shake. Get ready to get mad!

Did You Ever . . .

. . . feel how hot your hand is?

Hold the palm of your hand up against one of
your cheeks but not quite touching it. Hold it
still for a few moments. The heat from your
hand warms the air and your cheek feels it.
You'll find you really are "hot stuff"!

. . . taste an apple that tastes like an onion?

Cut a small piece of apple and a small piece of
onion. Hold the onion right under your nose and
smell the onion as you *chew* the apple. Ugh!
The apple tastes like an onion!

*. . . push a pin into a blown-up balloon without
having the balloon pop?*

Stick a piece of sticky tape on a balloon and
push a pin into the balloon through the tape.
SURPRISE—the balloon will not pop!

How To Put Twelve People in Eleven Beds

This is an old puzzle. It is impossible, yet you can *actually do it.* You will use eleven objects to take the place of "people"; pennies are handy.

Lay the eleven coins in a row on the table, then start your talk.

"This is the story of a hotel owner who solved a strange problem. His hotel had eleven bedrooms, but twelve people had come to spend the night.

"With a bit of juggling the hotel owner was able to fit the twelve people into the eleven beds. Let me show you how."

Push the first *two* pennies a bit to the left of the line.

"To start he put two people in the first bed. Just temporarily.

"He then placed the third person in the second bed."

Push the third penny beside the first two with a little space between.

"The fourth person goes into the third bed."
Push the fourth penny beside the third.
"The fifth person into the fourth bed."
Move the fifth penny beside the fourth.
"The sixth person goes into the fifth bed."
Move the sixth penny beside the fifth.

"The seventh person is put in the sixth bed."
Slide the seventh penny beside the sixth.
"The eighth person goes into the seventh bed."
Push the eighth penny beside the seventh.
"The ninth person into the eighth bed."
Slide the ninth penny next to the eighth.
"The tenth person goes into the ninth bed."
Slide the tenth penny beside the ninth.
"The *eleventh* person goes into the *tenth* bed.
Slide the eleventh, final, penny beside the tenth.

SO . . . we can now take the twelfth person out of the first bed where we put him temporarily . . ."

Take the second penny away from the first and drop it at the end of the row as you say,

". . . and put the *twelfth* person in the *eleventh* bed!"

You've apparently done it. You have actually put twelve people in eleven beds. How did you do it?

Hands Up!

Have you ever felt your arms levitate? That is, raise up all by themselves with apparently no help from you? The first time you try this old trick you will find it very spooky.

Stand in an open doorway with your hands hanging at your sides. Press the *backs* of your hands hard against the doorframe. HARD.

Push as hard as you can and slowly count to 20. Then step out of the doorway and allow your arms to *relax completely* as they hang by your sides.

If you really relax your arms they will slowly levitate. You will feel there is a mysterious force pulling them upward.

5

ARE YOU A MAGICIAN?

Fill a bowl with water and sprinkle lots of pepper on top. Use lots; really cover the water surface. (Don't sneeze!)

Rub your finger across a bar of soap.

Touch the middle of the pepper with *another* finger—*not* the one with the soap. Nothing happens.

Now touch the pepper with the finger you rubbed on the soap.

WOW . . . you must have a magician's finger!

Uncle George Is Watching You

This is a face you should easily recognize. It is the engraved portrait of George Washington as he appears on every one-dollar bill. It is a very mysterious picture!

Move the page back and forth and *watch George's eyes*. He seems to be facing sideways but he is looking straight at you. His eyes seem to follow you no matter which way you turn him.

When you look down on him from the top, he looks up at you. Look at him from the bottom and he looks down. Maybe he's watching you because he is worried about what you are going to spend him for.

Try a real dollar bill. He's there, still staring at you!

What You Are Thinking Of

Here's a trick to play on a group of friends.

"Please think of something, anything," you ask one of them. Then you pretend to concentrate and write something on a piece of paper. Nobody sees what you write.

"I am writing what you are thinking of on this piece of paper," you say. When you're done, fold the paper and hand it to your friend.

"See if I wrote what you are thinking of on the paper."

Your friend reads it.

"Did I write what you are thinking of?"

Your friend answers, "Yes."

Are you puzzled? Anyone watching will be, too. You won't be—neither will your friend. You both know *words* are fooling people.

Have you guessed what you write on the paper? You write "WHAT YOU ARE THINKING OF." Now read what you say again and you'll understand.

Your Two-Thumb Quick Trick

Here is a silly trick to do when nobody expects one.

Hold your left hand out with the fingers straight, so you are looking down on the back of it. Place your right hand flat on top, covering the left hand. Poke both thumbs out, one to the right, the other to the left.

Keeping them together, bring both hands up in front of your face and show them to a friend. When your friend looks, begin to wiggle your thumbs. For that moment you will seem to have a single hand with two thumbs.

Then, of course, your friend "catches on." Later, though, I'll bet you find your friend doing it too. It's foolish . . . but fun!

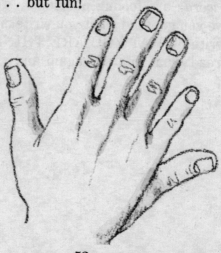

The Coin in the Tunnel

Unless you try this you won't believe it!

You'll need a small coin, a pencil, and a small cardboard matchbox.

Slip the coin in one end of the matchbox (empty of matches) *between* the *bottom* of the drawer and the outer box.

Hold the box in your hand with the end containing the coin downward.

The coin has entered the bottom of the "tunnel." Now you will make it rise *up* through it.

Using your other hand, tap the top end of the box with the pencil. Tap sharply again and again.

Keep tapping. You will see the coin poke out the top. It has "crawled" to the very top while inside the matchbox!

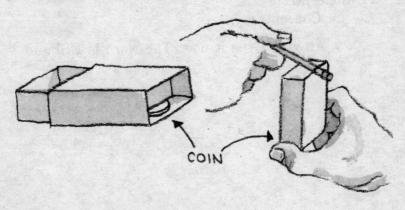

COIN

What's the Word?

Do this simple math for us . . .
  Think of any number.
  Double the number.
  Add 10 to the total.
  Divide the new number by 2.

Now:
  Subtract the number you first thought of.
  Remember the number you now have.

Now we can do a magic trick for you. Whatever number you ended with, turn to that page in this book. Begin with the title and count the same number of words as the number. Concentrate on that word.

  Concentrate . . .
   Concentrate . . .

  Ah yes, I see it now. The word is ESP.

How To Be a Memory Expert

When you read this you will think you could never do it. If you try you will amaze yourself and then you can amaze your friends.

You will need thirty small pieces of paper. On fifteen are printed "places." For example:

Bathroom	Bedroom	Kitchen
Closet	Porch	Hall
Sink	Stairway	Garage
Attic	Oven	Refrigerator
Basement	Bookcase	Living Room

On the other fifteen pieces print "things." For example:

Nose	Eyeball	Hot Dog
Knife	Paper Clip	Skunk
Elephant	Pogo Stick	Sneakers
Balloon	Elf	Deck of Cards
Clown	Snake	Sailboat

Now you can practice this trick by yourself until you prove how simple it is, but let us describe how you will present it for a friend.

Have your friend scatter the "places" papers on the table, writing side up, in any order. Explain that you have a fantastic memory and you will prove it.

Ask your friend to place a "thing" paper on each "place" paper. As he does, ask him to say "I am putting the (thing) in the (place)." He can select any place he chooses for any thing. You say that you will try to remember where everything is.

To further impress your friend ask him to try to remember too, and turn your back to him.

When he's done you ask him to name any "thing" and you immediately tell him the "place." You do this for every pair of papers. You can even do it the other way around. If he gives you a place you know what thing is there!

After you finish with a perfect score ask your friend to try to recall what he put where. He will get a few, but not all, and he'll be much more impressed with what you did.

How do you do it?

This trick really uses your memory, but a bit differently than usual. Let's say your friend says he put the "hot dog" in the kitchen. Most people would try to remember that by repeating "The hot dog is in the kitchen" over and over. Not you! As soon as you hear "hot dog" and "kitchen" close your eyes and make a *very funny picture* in your mind. Picture, perhaps, a giant hot dog with feet, hands, and a big mouth sitting at your kitchen table *eating you!* Did that make you smile? The next time you hear "hot dog" you will immediately see that picture in your mind. And where is that funny picture happening—in your kitchen, of course!

The "funny picture" way of remembering things is easy and fun. Just make a funny picture every time your friend gives you a "place" and a "thing." You will see an elephant stamping holes in your attic floor, a pair of sneakers in the refrigerator with salad dressing all over them, and a bookcase filled with balloons instead of books. Whatever funny picture you make up will jump right back into your mind later when you hear either word. It happens so easily it will amaze you.

Two final suggestions: First, use places in *your* home. If you don't have an attic, change that paper to name a place you do have. Second, change the things to things you can more easily form funny pictures with.

You will also find you can do this over again right away. New "funny pictures" will replace the old ones.

Don't tell your friends about your "funny pictures" trick for remembering and they will think you are a genius. They'll never know why you laugh when they say "oven" and "skunk."

Hypnotize a Handkerchief

Amaze yourself with a *clean, freshly washed* large handkerchief.

Tie a knot in one corner and hold the knot tightly in one hand.

Wrap your other hand tightly around the handkerchief just below the knot and pull it down over the cloth while you squeeze tightly.

When the hand comes off the bottom move it back up below the knot and repeat the squeeze and pull again. Do this half a dozen times.

Finally, on your last stroke, stop when you're near the bottom. Slowly, carefully, let go of the knot.

The handkerchief does not collapse or fall over. It stands straight up. You have "hypnotized" it.

If you show this trick to your friends they will want to examine the handkerchief to see what you have hidden inside . . . Then the surprise is on them!

The Surprising Seven

Shuffle a deck of cards well.

Cut the deck in half (as close as you can) and look at the card you cut to. Remember that card. Now put the deck back just the way it was, with your remembered card going in the center.

Pick up the deck and, without shuffling, deal one card at a time into four piles. Continue until all the deck is used and you have four equal piles before you.

Now look through the piles (without changing the order of the cards) and find the pile that contains your card. When you find it keep that pile and push the other three piles aside.

Hold the packet with your card face down and draw cards off the top one by one.

One . . . two . . . three . . . four . . . five . . . six . . .

SEVEN—turn the seventh one face up. IT IS YOUR CARD. I found it, and I'm just a book. It must be real magic!

Of course, it's not real magic and sometimes you will miss. If the seventh card is not yours please try it again for us. The second time never fails!

The Magic Doctor

"Oh, Mom, look at the awful blister I've got."

You show your finger and your mother sees a big bubble of skin on it.

"Oh, that's too bad. It looks sore, is it?" she asks.

"Yes," you answer. "So I think I'll make it go away."

"How can you do that?"

"With a touch of magic."

Your other hand rubs away the blister.

You need only one object to give yourself a very real looking make-believe blister—a washer. Get one (that's used with bolts) having a hole about the size of a lead pencil. Put it in your pocket and squeeze the washer between your forefinger and thumb. Squeeze real hard. When you take your hand out (leaving the washer behind) you will have two bubbles of skin—one on your thumb and one on your finger.

They will look exactly like blisters, but they aren't. They will not last long so keep squeezing the washer until just before you show your finger. If you rub them a little they vanish instantly!

6

FOR YOU
AND YOUR
FRIENDS

"How would you like a Hertz Doughnut?"

"What's that?"

Step down on your friend's toes (but not *too* hard).

"Hurts, don't it!"

How To Be a Fortune-Teller

"I am a palm reader. Would you like me to tell your fortune?"

Your friend agrees and holds out her hand. You stare deeply into her palm.

"Ah, yes. I see a big crack on this side . . ."

Point to a line on her palm.

". . . and a crack on this side."

Point to another line on the other side of the palm.

"Yes. Your future is very clear. You will have another crack soon . . . here . . . right in the middle . . . AND HERE IT IS!"

Give her palm a good hard slap and run. If you don't we can tell you what your fortune will be!

Just Three Sticks

So your friend has a candy bar and won't offer any to you? Well, we'll just see about that. Here is a sure-fire, never-fail, sneaky trick that will catch anyone anytime.

Borrow the candy from your friend and place it on the table. Arrange three little twigs around it and lay a dime beside that. Point to the dime and say, "I'll bet you that dime that you can't answer 'Three little sticks' to my next three questions."

Your friend will take the bet. It sounds very simple to win your dime.

"Of course if you don't answer 'Three little sticks' you have to give me the candy bar, okay?"

"Okay," your friend will reply.

"What's around your candy bar?"

"Three little sticks."

"What does two plus two equal?"

"Three little sticks."

It seems your friend is about to win. The game is so simple for him. But you have just been setting him up and you're ready to zing him. Your final question:

"What will you take for your candy bar?"

If he says "Three little sticks," give them to him. If he doesn't say it you've won his candy bar anyway!

This Is Thursday

Hold your hand with the thumb and first finger touching. Raise the hand toward your face and look through the "hole" at a friend.

"Do you know what this is?"

Your friend will be puzzled. She'll have no idea what you are doing.

"This is Thursday!"

Now your friend is even more puzzled. You will have to make things clear.

Move your thumb so it presses against your *little* finger.

"This is Monday!"

Now move your thumb so it presses against your *ring* finger.

"And this is Tuesday!"

Move the thumb again and press it against the *middle* finger.

"This is Wednesday!"

Finally press your thumb against the *first* finger, back where it started.

"So this must be Thursday!"

Your friend will probably just shake her head and feel sorry for you.

A Two-Second Offer

OPEN THIS CARD IN TWO SECONDS
AND YOU CAN HAVE THE DOLLAR
THAT'S INSIDE.

It sounds like an offer that's too simple. And it is!

There is no dollar inside! Why? Because your friend has no chance of winning, of course.

No, you don't glue the card shut or anything like that. Your friend *can* open the card *easily*— but nobody ever does.

What's the catch? Look at the illustration.

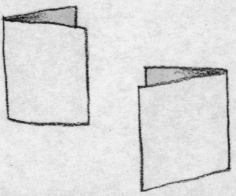

Most cards open from the right edge, like a book. People are used to cards opening like that. Make your card open from the left side, the opposite of the usual way. Use stiff cardboard and crease it sharply. Your friend will read it quickly and be in a big hurry to open it—but from the right edge!

The Dribble Cup

A "Dribble Glass" is a dirty trick that has been around for a hundred years or more. Years ago you couldn't make one because a tiny hole had to be drilled through glass. Now that paper cups have been invented, however, that hole is a cinch to "drill."

Push a pin or needle (nothing larger) through one side of a paper cup toward the bottom. Make a small circle around it, with a pencil, so you can spot where the hole is exactly. Put this cup beside some similar cups without holes and you're ready.

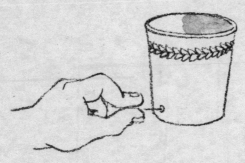

Your victim—er, "friend"—wants a drink of water. So do you. Pour yourself one in a regular cup and set it down on the table. Pick up the Dribble Cup. Pick it up with your thumb pressing against the tiny hole and wrap your fingers around the other side.

Fill the Dribble Cup. As long as your thumb covers the hole, the water will stay inside. Everything will look perfectly normal and your friend will suspect nothing.

Pick up your own cup with your other hand as you hand the Dribble Cup to your victim.

Chances are very slim that his hand will cover the tiny hole. What do you think the cup will be doing?

You are right—dribbling!

Wet-Penny Fortune-Telling

You will need a penny, a paper cup full of water, and an unsuspecting friend for this neat dirty trick.

Have the penny and cup of water on the table. Tell your friend that you will use the "wet-penny" method of fortune-telling to find out about the future. First you will demonstrate how it works.

Hold your hands behind your back. Ask your friend to dip the penny in the water and press it hard against your forehead. The water and suction will cause the coin to cling to your skin.

Ask, "How many times will I be married?" Explain that you will now shake your head until the penny falls off. Each shake means a time you will marry. You shake your head, and after two or three shakes the penny falls.

Now ask your friend to try it.

Dip the penny and stick it to your friend's forehead. Ask, "How many times will you marry?" You continue with other questions and use the head shakes to get the answers. "How many boy or girl friends will you have? How many years before you marry?"

Now for the dirty work. Your friend is getting used to the game. Your friend doesn't expect anything different to happen. BUT, on the last dip, drop the penny into the water and bring out your finger and thumb as though they still held the coin.

When your hand is at your friend's forehead turn it so you can press your wet fingernail against the skin. It feels wet and hard, just like the penny.

Take your hand away and your friend will still have the *feeling* of something on the forehead just as before.

Ask, "How many children will you have?"

Your friend's head shakes and shakes and shakes and shakes. Your friend had better catch on soon or he or she will have more children than that old woman who lived in a shoe!

A Very Cheap Trick

You will lose this bet and you will lose your money, but you will still trick your friend. Not only that, but you will come out better.

Say that your friend has a candy bar that you would like. Ask him to place it on the table. Cover it over with a sheet of paper.

Toss a penny on the table.

"I'll bet you this penny that I can eat that candy without touching the paper," you say.

That seems impossible enough. Your friend will take your bet.

What do you do? A real nasty.

QUICKLY! Toss the paper aside, grab the candy, and gobble it down.

Then toss the penny to your friend and say, "Sorry, YOU WIN!"

A Real Dirty One

There are two china saucers on the table and two chairs beside it. You are about to trick your friend and he doesn't even suspect it.

"I'll bet you can't do everything I do for two minutes without making a mistake," you challenge.

You assure him you will move very slowly so he can watch carefully. He agrees.

You sit in one chair. He sits in the other.

You wave your hand over the saucer. He does the same.

You pick up the saucer in your left hand. He does the same with the other saucer. You compliment him on not having made a mistake so far. Be sure someone is timing you. This takes about one minute, so you have one more to go.

Rub your finger three times on top of the saucer and draw it across your forehead. Give him time to duplicate your actions. He does. No mistakes.

Rub your finger three times on the bottom of the saucer without turning it over. HOLD YOUR FINGER THERE until he has done the exact same thing and is holding his finger there too.

Quickly take your finger out from under the saucer and rub it twice across your forehead. Then down your nose. Then across your chin. Then touch

71

both cheeks. Give him just enough time so he has
to rush to keep up.

Keep up the rubbing, in different places, until
your timekeeper says the two minutes are up.

Congratulate your friend! He has won. He did
not make a single mistake.

On the other hand, you haven't really lost anything and he looks so silly right now everyone in
the room is laughing.

He'll know why when he looks in a mirror!

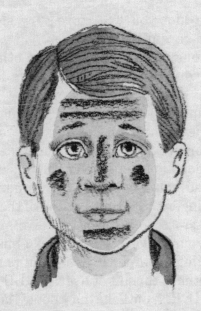

What did you do?

You used one thing your friend didn't know
about. A candle.

Before your friend came you held the bottom of one saucer in a lighted candle flame. (Be sure to have an adult help you with this.) The fire doesn't hurt the china but it does cover it with black soot. Move the saucer around in the flame to be sure the bottom is really black. This, of course, is the saucer your friend gets!

Now you know. Your friend ends up "painting" lines and spots all over his face. Everyone but him can see them.

Your friend will see them in a mirror.

Get ready to run.

The soot will wash off with soap and water
—but not *too* easily!

Your Newspaper Weather Forecaster

"I'm very concerned about the weather so I have invented a surefire weather forecaster that anyone can make out of a single sheet of newspaper," you tell a friend.

You show a sheet from an old newpaper. Act very serious.

"First you must take the sheet and squeeze it into a small tight ball."

Crumple it from one corner and work it into the shape of a rough ball. Pretend that it is very important that the ball be made in exactly the correct way.

"Now here's how it works. When you go to bed, open your window and place the newspaper forecaster on the window ledge. Do you understand so far?"

Your friend nods in agreement.

"Good. Now tomorrow morning reach out and pick up the forecaster. If you find it is *wet*, then it's *raining*. If it's *dry* the weather is *fair*. But if you find the ball is *gone* . . ."

Toss the ball away.

". . . then it's *windy!*"

Now your friend will know for sure that you're a nut!

Awful Things To Say

(When your friend is singing.)
"What did you do with the money?"
Puzzled. "What money?"
"The money your mother gave you for the singing
   lessons!"

"Hey, you have a string hanging from your dress."
Friend looks down.
"Oh, excuse me, that's your leg."

(Looking at a friend, shaking your head.)
"I told your doctor."
Puzzled. "You told my doctor what?"
"I told your doctor brain transplants wouldn't
   work!"

"You'd give a headache to an aspirin!"

The Last Thought

Have you ever read any "sound-the-same" words? These are words that are spelled differently but when they are spoken they all sound the same. Here's a nice example to finish our book with . . .

WHEEL OF VIEW

Say it.
Now say

OUI LUF EWE

These sound the same as

WE LOVE YOU!

And we do! Thanks for letting us share your book with you.